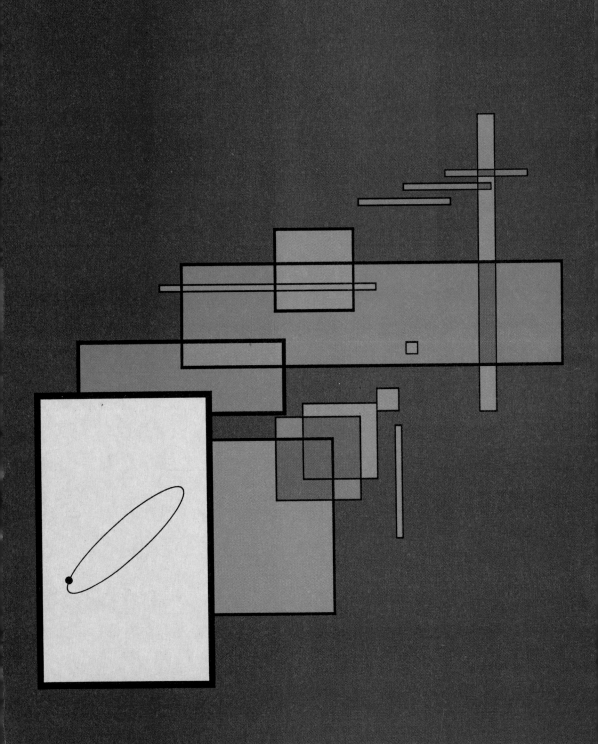

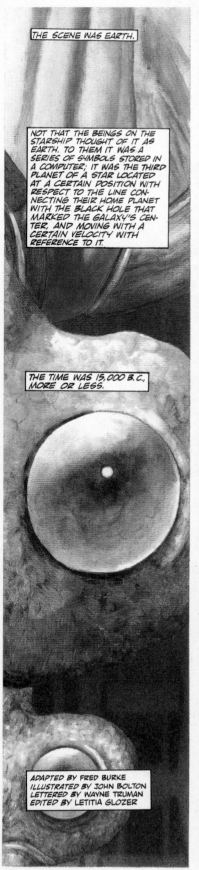

THE SCENE WAS EARTH.

NOT THAT THE BEINGS ON THE STARSHIP THOUGHT OF IT AS EARTH. TO THEM IT WAS A SERIES OF SYMBOLS STORED IN A COMPUTER; IT WAS THE THIRD PLANET OF A STAR LOCATED AT A CERTAIN POSITION WITH RESPECT TO THE LINE CONNECTING THEIR HOME PLANET WITH THE BLACK HOLE THAT MARKED THE GALAXY'S CENTER, AND MOVING WITH A CERTAIN VELOCITY WITH REFERENCE TO IT.

THE TIME WAS 15,000 B.C., MORE OR LESS.

ADAPTED BY FRED BURKE
ILLUSTRATED BY JOHN BOLTON
LETTERED BY WAYNE TRUMAN
EDITED BY LETITIA GLOZER

NOT THAT THE BEINGS ON THE STARSHIP THOUGHT OF IT AS 15,000 B.C. TO THEM, IT WAS A CERTAIN PERIOD OF TIME MARKED OFF ACCORDING TO THEIR LOCAL SYSTEM.

Isaac Asimov's
Nothing
For
Nothing

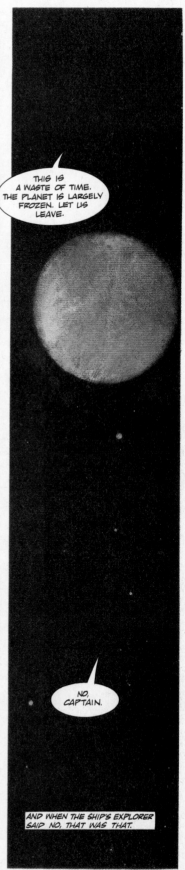

THIS IS A WASTE OF TIME. THE PLANET IS LARGELY FROZEN. LET US LEAVE.

NO, CAPTAIN.

AND WHEN THE SHIP'S EXPLORER SAID NO, THAT WAS THAT.

AS LONG AS A STARSHIP WAS IN SPACE, THE CAPTAIN WAS SUPREME, BUT PLACE THAT SHIP IN ORBIT ABOUT A PLANET AND THE EXPLORER COULD NOT BE CHALLENGED. HE KNEW WORLDS! THAT WAS HIS SPECIALTY.

AND THIS EXPLORER WAS IN AN IMPREGNABLE POSITION. IT HAD BEEN HE AND HE ALONE WHO WAS RESPONSIBLE FOR THE FACT THAT THIS STARSHIP HAD WON THREE AWARDS FOR EXCELLENCE FOR THE WORK DONE IN THE LAST THREE EXPEDITIONS. THREE FOR THREE.

SO WHEN THE EXPLORER SAID "NO," THE CAPTAIN COULD NOT DREAM OF "YES." IN THE UNLIKELY CASE THAT HE WOULD HAVE DREAMED IT, THE CREW WOULD HAVE MUTINIED. AN AWARD FOR EXCELLENCE MIGHT BE, TO THE CAPTAIN, A PLEASANT SPECTRAL DISK TO SUSPEND IN THE MAIN SALON; BUT TO THE CREW, IT MEANT A SPECTACULAR ADDITION TO TAKE-HOME PAY. AND THIS EXPLORER HAD BROUGHT THEM THAT THREE TIMES. THREE FOR THREE.

SURELY THAT'S NOT UNPRECEDENTED.

AND THAT WAS THAT, OF COURSE. THERE WERE AT LEAST HALF A TRILLION PLANETARY WORLDS IN THE GALAXY, IF ONE ONLY COUNTED THOSE ASSOCIATED WITH STARS.

EVEN WITH COMPUTERS TO HELP, NO STARSHIP COULD KNOW THEM ALL; BUT AN EXPERIENCED EXPLORER, BY DINT OF LACKING INTEREST IN ANYTHING ELSE, OF STUDYING EVERY EXPLORATORY REPORT PUBLISHED, OF CONSIDERING ENDLESS CORRELATIONS, AND-- PRESUMABLY-- PLAYING WITH STATISTICS EVEN IN HIS SLEEP, GREW TO HAVE WHAT SEEMED TO OTHERS A MYSTICAL INTUITION ABOUT SUCH THINGS.

WHAT IS STRANGE ABOUT THIS ONE?

THE PATTERN HERE IS STRANGE. I AM NOT SURE EXACTLY HOW OR EXACTLY WHY, BUT THE PATTERN OF LIFE AND OF INTELLIGENCE IS STRANGE. WE MUST EXAMINE IT MORE CAREFULLY.

WE'LL HAVE TO SEND OUT PROBES IN FULL INTERLOCKING PROGRAM.

IT'LL TAKE WEEKS! IS THIS ABSOLUTELY NECESSARY?

NO STRANGE WORLD SHOULD BE LEFT UNEXAMINED.

THE PRELIMINARY PROBE SHOWS INTELLIGENCE-- AND ON A FROZEN WORLD.

I RATHER THINK SO.

THE PROBES BROUGHT BACK EXACTLY WHAT THE CAPTAIN EXPECTED; AND IN GREAT DETAIL.

"INTELLIGENT SPECIES RATHER REMINISCENT OF THE LESSER BREEDS OF THE INNER PROXIMAL REGIONS OF THE FIFTH ARM OF THE GALAXY." THIS SPECIES MAY BE OF INTEREST TO MENTOLOGISTS, BUT THEY'RE ONLY AT THE FIRST LEVEL OF TECHNOLOGY! THERE'S NOTHING USEFUL HERE!

STRANGE! SUMMON THE TRADER.

TO WHAT END, EXPLORER? WHAT CAN WE EXPECT AT THIS LEVEL?

THEY HAVE TOOLS...

STONE! BONE! WOOD! OR THIS PLANET'S EQUIVALENT. *THAT'S* ALL! SURELY WE CAN FIND NOTHING IN THAT.

AND YET THERE IS SOMETHING STRANGE IN THE PATTERN.

MAY I KNOW WHAT THAT MIGHT BE, EXPLORER?

IF I KNEW WHAT IT MIGHT BE, CAPTAIN, IT WOULD NOT BE STRANGE, AND I WOULD NOT HAVE TO FIND OUT. REALLY, CAPTAIN--I MUST INSIST ON THE TRADER.

THE CAPTAIN MIGHT NAVIGATE A STARSHIP AND THE EXPLORER MIGHT DETECT USEFUL CIVILIZATIONS BY THE MOST TENUOUS OF SIGNS; BUT IN THE FINAL CLUTCH, IT WAS THE TRADER AND HIS TEAM WHO FACED THE ALIENS AND WHO PLUCKED OUT OF THEIR MINDS AND CULTURE THAT WHICH WAS USEFUL AND GAVE IN RETURN SOMETHING *THEY* FOUND USEFUL.

THIS WAS DONE AT GREAT RISK. THE ALIEN ECOLOGY MUST NOT BE DISRUPTED; ALIEN INTELLIGENCES MUST NOT BE HARMED, NOT EVEN TO SAVE ONE'S OWN LIFE. THERE WERE GOOD REASONS FOR THAT ON THE COSMIC SCALE AND TRADERS WERE AMPLY REWARDED FOR THE RISKS THEY RAN--BUT WHY RUN *USELESS* RISKS?

THERE IS NOTHING THERE.

MY INTERPRETATION OF THE PROBE'S DATA IS THAT WE'RE DEALING WITH SEMI-INTELLIGENT ANIMALS. THEIR USEFULNESS IS NIL. THEIR DANGER IS GREAT.

WE KNOW HOW TO DEAL WITH TRULY INTELLIGENT ALIENS, AND TRADER TEAMS ARE RARELY KILLED BY THEM. WHO KNOWS HOW THESE ANIMALS WILL REACT-- AND YOU KNOW WE ARE NOT ALLOWED TO DEFEND OURSELVES PROPERLY.

BUT, TRADER, THESE ANIMALS, IF THEY ARE NO MORE THAN THAT, HAVE INTERESTINGLY ADAPTED THEMSELVES TO THE ICE. THERE ARE SUBTLE VARIATIONS IN THE PATTERN HERE I DO NOT UNDERSTAND; BUT MY CONSIDERED OPINION IS THAT THEY WILL NOT BE DANGEROUS AND THAT THEY MAY EVEN BE USEFUL.

I FEEL THEY ARE WORTH CLOSER EXAMINATION.

WHAT CAN BE GAINED FROM A STONE AGE INTELLIGENCE?

THAT IS FOR YOU TO FIND OUT.

OF COURSE, THAT IS WHAT IT COMES TO--FOR *US* TO FIND OUT.

THE TRADER KNEW FULL WELL THE HISTORY AND PURPOSE OF THE STARSHIP EXPEDITIONS. THERE HAD BEEN A TIME, A MILLION YEARS BEFORE, WHEN THERE HAD BEEN NO TRADERS, EXPLORERS, OR CAPTAINS BUT ONLY ANCESTRAL ANIMALS WITH DEVELOPING MINDS AND A STONE AGE TECHNOLOGY--MUCH LIKE THE ANIMALS ON THE WORLD THEY WERE NOW ORBITING.

HOW SLOW THE ADVANCE, HOW PAINFULLY SLOW THE SELF-GENERATED PROCESS--UNTIL THE THIRD-LEVEL CIVILIZATION HAD BEEN REACHED. THEN HAD COME THE STARSHIPS AND THE CHANCE OF CROSS-FERTILIZATION OF CULTURES. THEN HAD COME PROGRESS.

WITH RESPECT, EXPLORER...I GRANT YOU INTUITIONAL EXPERIENCE. WILL YOU GRANT MY PRACTICAL EXPERIENCE, THOUGH IT IS LESS DRAMATIC? THERE IS NO WAY IN WHICH ANYTHING BELOW A THIRD-LEVEL CIVILIZATION CAN HAVE ANYTHING WE CAN USE.

THAT IS A GENERALIZATION THAT MAY OR MAY NOT BE TRUE.

WITH RESPECT, EXPLORER. IT IS TRUE. AND EVEN IF THOSE--THOSE SEMI-ANIMALS HAD SOMETHING WE COULD USE, AND I CAN'T IMAGINE WHAT IT MIGHT BE, WHAT CAN WE GIVE THEM IN EXCHANGE?

THE EXPLORER WAS SILENT.

AT THIS LEVEL, THERE IS NO WAY IN WHICH A PROTO-INTELLIGENCE CAN ACCEPT AN ALIEN STIMULATION. THE MENTOLOGISTS ARE AGREED ON THAT. PROGRESS MUST BE SELF-GENERATED UNTIL AT LEAST THE SECOND LEVEL IS REACHED. AND WE MUST MAKE A RETURN; WE CAN TAKE NOTHING FOR NOTHING.

AND THAT MAKES SENSE, OF COURSE. BY STIMULATING THESE INTELLIGENCES TO ADVANCE, WE CAN HARVEST THEM AGAIN AT A LATER VISIT.

I DON'T CARE ABOUT THE REASON FOR IT. IT IS PART OF THE TRADITION OF MY PROFESSION. WE DO NO HARM UNDER ANY CONDITIONS AND WE GIVE IN RETURN FOR WHAT WE TAKE.

HERE THERE IS NOTHING WE WILL WANT TO TAKE, AND EVEN IF WE FIND SOMETHING, THERE WILL BE NOTHING THAT WE CAN GIVE IN RETURN. WE WASTE TIME.

I ASK YOU TO VISIT SOME CENTER OF POPULATION, TRADER. I WILL ABIDE BY YOUR DECISION WHEN YOU RETURN.

AND THAT WAS THAT, TOO.

FOR TWO DAYS THE SMALL TRADER MODULE FLASHED OVER THE SURFACE OF THE PLANET SEARCHING FOR ANY EVIDENCE OF A REASONABLE LEVEL OF TECHNOLOGY. THERE WAS NONE.

RECORD. RECORD THE ANIMALS, BOTH UNINTELLIGENT AND SUPPOSEDLY INTELLIGENT, AND ANY ARTIFACTS OF THEIRS WE CAN FIND. MAKE SURE THE RECORDS ARE THOROUGHLY HOLOGRAPHIC.

THE ATMOSPHERE WOULD SUPPORT THEM, BUT THE FEELING OF EXPOSURE TO THE RAW WINDS OF AN OPEN PLANET WOULD DISCOMMODE THEM, EVEN IF THE ATMOSPHERE AND TEMPERATURE WERE PERFECT-- WHICH THEY WEREN'T.

THE TRADER AND HIS CREW DID NOT TRY TO COMMUNICATE DIRECTLY OR TO MAKE FRIENDLY GESTURES. WHO KNEW WHAT GESTURE MIGHT BE CONSIDERED FRIENDLY BY AN ALIEN?

BUT, MAESTRO, WE CAN ALREADY SEE--

THE TRADER SET UP A MENTAL FIELD, INSTEAD, AND SATURATED IT WITH THE VIBRATIONS OF HARMLESSNESS AND PEACE AND HOPED THAT THE MENTAL FIELDS OF THE CREATURES WERE SUFFICIENTLY ADVANCED TO RESPOND.

A COMPLETE SEARCH COULD TAKE YEARS, BUT WAS SCARCELY WORTH IT. THE HIGHEST TECHNOLOGY WAS ALWAYS FLAUNTED, FOR IT HAD NO ENEMY. THAT WAS THE UNIVERSAL EXPERIENCE OF TRADERS EVERYWHERE.

WE CAN ALREADY SEE, BUT WE MUST HAVE A RECORD TO CONVINCE OUR EXPLORER OUT OF HIS DREAMS OR WE'LL REMAIN HERE FOREVER.

THE GRAVITY WAS A TOUCH HIGH, AS WAS THE LIGHT LEVEL, BUT THEY COULD BEAR IT.

HE IS A GOOD EXPLORER.

WE'LL LAND HERE. IT SEEMS TO BE A GOOD-SIZED CONCENTRATION OF INTELLIGENCES. WE CAN DO NO BETTER.

PERHAPS THEY WERE, FOR A FEW CREPT BACK AND WATCHED. THE TRADER THOUGHT HE DETECTED FUGITIVE THOUGHTS--BUT THAT SEEMED UNLIKELY FOR FIRST-LEVEL BEINGS AND HE DID NOT FOLLOW THEM UP.

WHAT CAN WE DO WITH EVEN THESE, MAESTRO?

HE HAS BEEN A GOOD EXPLORER, BUT DOES THAT MEAN HE WILL BE GOOD FOREVER? HIS VERY SUCCESSES HAVE MADE HIM ACCEPT HIMSELF AT TOO HIGH AN EVALUATION, PERHAPS. SO WE MUST CONVINCE HIM OF REALITY-- IF WE CAN.

THE TRADER WAS RELIEVED BY THE ALIENS' RETREAT. ANY SIGN OF NON-BELLIGERENCE WAS WELCOME TO THOSE WHO WERE NOT PERMITTED TO DEFEND THEMSELVES.

MAESTRO! HERE! COME QUICKLY!

SPECIFIC DIRECTIONS WERE NOT GIVEN. THE TRADER HAD TO FOLLOW THE BEAM. OTHER MEMBERS OF THE CREW WERE CONVERGING, BUT HE KNEW HE WOULD ARRIVE FIRST.

WHAT IS IT?

THIS IS A NATURAL HOLLOW, NOT A TECHNOLOGICAL PRODUCT.

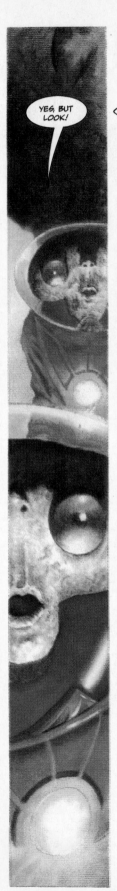

YES, BUT LOOK!

STAY AWAY! REPEAT-- STAY AWAY!

IS THIS OF TECHNOLOGICAL ORIGIN?

YES, MAESTRO, YOU CAN SEE IT IS ONLY PARTIALLY COMPLETED. I FOUND ONE OF THE INTELLIGENT CREATURES AT WORK IN HERE. THIS IS HIS LIGHT SOURCE--BURNING VEGETATION. THESE ARE HIS TOOLS.

AND WHERE IS HE?

HE FLED.

DID YOU ACTUALLY SEE HIM?

I RECORDED HIM.

HAVE YOU EVER SEEN ANYTHING LIKE THIS?

NO, MAESTRO.

OR HEARD OF ANYTHING LIKE THIS?

NO, MAESTRO.

8

ASTONISHING!

MAESTRO. WHAT DO WE DO?

EH?

THIS WILL SURELY WIN OUR SHIP STILL A FOURTH PRIZE.

SURELY-- IF WE COULD TAKE IT.

I--I HAVE ALREADY RECORDED IT.

EH? WHAT IS THE USE OF THAT? WE HAVE NOTHING TO GIVE IN EXCHANGE.

BUT WE HAVE THIS OF THEIRS. GIVE THEM ANYTHING IN EXCHANGE!

WHAT ARE YOU SAYING?! THEY ARE TOO PRIMITIVE TO ACCEPT ANYTHING WE COULD GIVE THEM. IT WILL SURELY BE A MILLION YEARS BEFORE THEY COULD POSSIBLY ACCEPT SUG- GESTIONS OF EXOGENOUS ORIGIN--WE WILL HAVE TO DESTROY THE RECORDING.

BUT WE KNOW, MAESTRO!

THEN WE MUST NEVER TALK ABOUT IT. OUR CRAFT HAS ITS ETHICS AND ITS TRADITIONS. YOU KNOW THAT. NOTHING FOR NOTHING!

EVEN THIS?

EVEN THIS.

THE TRADER'S STERNLY IMPLACABLE SET OF EXPRESSION WAS TINGED WITH UNBEARABLE SORROW AND DESPITE HIS "EVEN THIS" HE STOOD IRRESOLUTE.

TRY GIVING THEM SOMETHING, MAESTRO.

OF WHAT USE WOULD THAT BE?

OF WHAT HARM?

IT IS A FORM OF VISUAL ART.

PLAYING WITH COLOR?

AND SHAPE-- TO MOST STARTLING EFFECT. OBSERVE!

UGLY OBJECTS.

THE HOLOGRAPHIC RECORDING BROUGHT THE HERD TO A HALT, CLAMPED IT DOWN TO A STILL. IT MAGNIFIED, AND A SINGLE BEAST FILLED THE VIEW.

OBSERVE THIS ANIMAL...

...AND NOW OBSERVE THIS ARTIFICIAL COMPOSITION OF A PRIMITIVE CONCOCTION OF OIL AND COLORED MINERAL, WHICH WE FOUND SMEARED ON THE WALL OF A CAVE.

WHAT A PECULIAR SIMILARITY...

THERE IT WAS AGAIN! NOT QUITE THE ANIMAL AS HOLOGRAPHED-- FLAT, BUT VIBRANT.

NOT PECULIAR-- DELIBERATE!

I HAVE PREPARED A PRESENTATION FOR THE ENTIRE STARSHIP, BUT I MUST SHOW IT TO YOU FIRST, EXPLORER--WITH DEEP RESPECT AND WITH APOLOGIES FOR MASKED THOUGHTS.

YOU WERE RIGHT. THERE **WAS** SOMETHING STRANGE ABOUT THIS PLANET. THOUGH THE INTELLIGENCES WERE BARELY FIRST LEVEL AND THEIR TECHNOLOGY PRIMITIVE IN THE EXTREME, THEY HAD DEVELOPED A CONCEPT WE HAVE NEVER HAD--AND ONE THAT, TO MY KNOWLEDGE, WE HAVE NEVER ENCOUNTERED ON ANY OTHER WORLD.

I CANNOT IMAGINE WHAT IT MIGHT BE.

THE CAPTAIN WAS QUITE AWARE THAT TRADERS SOMETIMES OVERPRAISED THEIR PURCHASES TO MAGNIFY THEIR OWN WORTH.

THE EXPLORER SAID NOTHING. HE WAS THE MORE UNEASY OF THE TWO.

10

THERE WERE DOZENS OF SUCH FIGURES IN DIFFERENT POSES--OF DIFFERENT ANIMALS. THE LIKENESSES WERE TOO DETAILED TO BE FORTUITOUS. IMAGINE THE BOLDNESS OF THE CONCEPTION--TO PLACE COLORS IN PLEASING SHAPES AND COMBINATIONS, AND IN SUCH A WAY AS TO DECEIVE THE EYE INTO THINKING IT IS LOOKING AT A REAL OBJECT. THESE ORGANISMS HAVE DEVISED AN ART THAT REPRESENTS REALITY.

AND THAT'S NOT ALL. WE FOUND IT DONE IN THREE DIMENSIONS ALSO. THESE ARE CLEARLY INTENDED TO REPRESENT THEMSELVES.

DID YOU SEE THESE MANUFACTURED?

NO, THAT I DID NOT, CAPTAIN. ONE OF MY MEN SAW A PLANETARY BEING SMEARING COLOR ON ONE OF THE CAVE REPRESENTATIONS, BUT THESE WE FOUND ALREADY FORMED. STILL, NO OTHER EXPLANATION IS POSSIBLE THAN THAT THEY WERE DELIBERATELY SHAPED. THESE OBJECTS COULD NOT HAVE ASSUMED THESE SHAPES BY CHANCE PROCESSES.

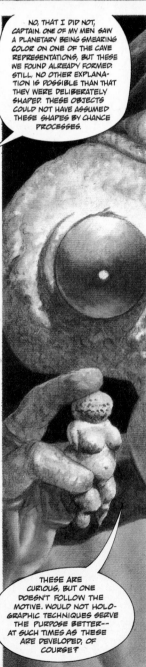

THESE ARE CURIOUS, BUT ONE DOESN'T FOLLOW THE MOTIVE. WOULD NOT HOLOGRAPHIC TECHNIQUES SERVE THE PURPOSE BETTER-- AT SUCH TIMES AS THESE ARE DEVELOPED, OF COURSE?

THESE PRIMITIVES HAVE NO CONCEPTION THAT HOLOGRAPHY COULD SOMEDAY BE DEVELOPED AND COULD NOT WAIT THE MILLION YEARS REQUIRED. THEN, TOO, MAYBE HOLOGRAPHY IS *NOT* BETTER. IF YOU COMPARE THE REPRESENTATIONS WITH THE ORIGINALS YOU WILL NOTICE THAT THE REPRESENTATIONS ARE SIMPLIFIED AND DISTORTED IN SUBTLE WAYS DESIGNED TO BRING CERTAIN CHARACTERISTICS INTO FOCUS.

I BELIEVE THIS FORM OF ART *IMPROVES* ON THE ORIGINAL IN SOME WAYS AND CERTAINLY HAS SOMETHING DIFFERENT TO SAY.

I STAND IN AWE OF YOUR ABILITIES, EXPLORER. CAN YOU EXPLAIN HOW YOU SENSED THE UNIQUENESS OF THIS INTELLIGENCE?

I DID NOT SUSPECT THIS AT ALL. IT IS INTERESTING AND I SEE ITS WORTH-- ALTHOUGH I WONDER IF WE COULD OURSELVES PROPERLY CONTROL OUR COLORS AND SHAPES IN ORDER TO FORCE THEM INTO SUCH REPRESENTATIONAL FORM. YET THIS DOES NOT MATCH THE UNEASE WITHIN ME--

--WHAT I WONDER IS HOW YOU CAME INTO POSSESSION OF THESE! WHAT DID YOU GIVE IN EXCHANGE? IT IS *THERE* I SEE THE STRANGENESS LIE!

WELL, IN A WAY YOU'RE RIGHT. QUITE STRANGE. I DID NOT THINK I COULD GIVE ANYTHING SINCE THE ORGANISMS ARE SO PRIMITIVE, BUT THIS DISCOVERY SEEMED TOO IMPORTANT TO SACRIFICE WITHOUT SOME EFFORT.

I THEREFORE CHOSE FROM AMONG THE GROUP OF BEINGS ONE WHOSE MENTAL FIELD SEEMED SOMEWHAT MORE INTENSE THAN THAT OF THE OTHERS AND ATTEMPTED TO TRANSFER TO HIM A GIFT IN EXCHANGE.

AND SUCCEEDED. OF COURSE.

YES, I SUCCEEDED. THE BEINGS KILL SUCH ANIMALS AS THEY REPRESENT IN COLOR, BY THROWING LONG STICKS TIPPED WITH SHARPENED STONE. THESE PENETRATE THE HIDES OF THE ANIMALS, WOUND AND WEAKEN THEM. THEY CAN THEN BE KILLED BY THE BEINGS WHO ARE INDIVIDUALLY SMALLER AND WEAKER THAN THE ANIMAL THEY HUNT.

I POINTED OUT THAT A SMALLER, STONE-TIPPED STICK COULD BE HURLED FORWARD WITH GREATER FORCE AND EFFECT AND WITH A LONGER RANGE IF A CORD UNDER TENSION WERE USED AS THE MECHANISM OF PROPULSION.

SUCH DEVICES HAVE BEEN ENCOUNTERED AMONG PRIMITIVE INTELLIGENCES WHICH WERE, HOWEVER, FAR ADVANCED BEYOND THESE. PALEOMENTALISTS CALL IT A BOW-AND-ARROW.

HOW COULD THE KNOWLEDGE BE ABSORBED? IT COULDN'T BE—NOT AT THIS LEVEL OF DEVELOPMENT.

BUT IT *WAS*. UNMISTAKEABLY. THE RESPONSE OF THE MENTAL FIELD WAS ONE OF INSIGHT AT ALMOST UNBEARABLE INTENSITY. SURELY YOU DO NOT THINK I WOULD HAVE TAKEN THESE ART OBJECTS, WERE THEY TWENTY TIMES AS VALUABLE, IF I HAD NOT BEEN CONVINCED THAT I HAD MADE A RETURN? NOTHING FOR NOTHING, CAPTAIN.

THERE IS THE STRANGENESS. TO ACCEPT.

BUT SURELY, TRADER, WE CANNOT DO THIS. THEY ARE NOT READY. WE ARE HARMING THEM. THEY WILL USE THE BOW-AND-ARROW TO WOUND EACH OTHER AND NOT THE BEASTS ALONE.

WE DO NOT HARM THEM AND WE *DID* NOT HARM THEM. WHAT *THEY* DO TO EACH OTHER AND WHERE THEY END AS A RESULT, A MILLION YEARS FROM NOW, IS THEIR CONCERN.

BUT THEY ACCEPTED. AND THEY FLOURISH AMID THE ICE. AND IN TWENTY THOUSAND YEARS, IT WILL BE *OUR* CONCERN.

HE KNEW THEY WOULD NOT BELIEVE HIM, AND HE DESPAIRED.

12

The End

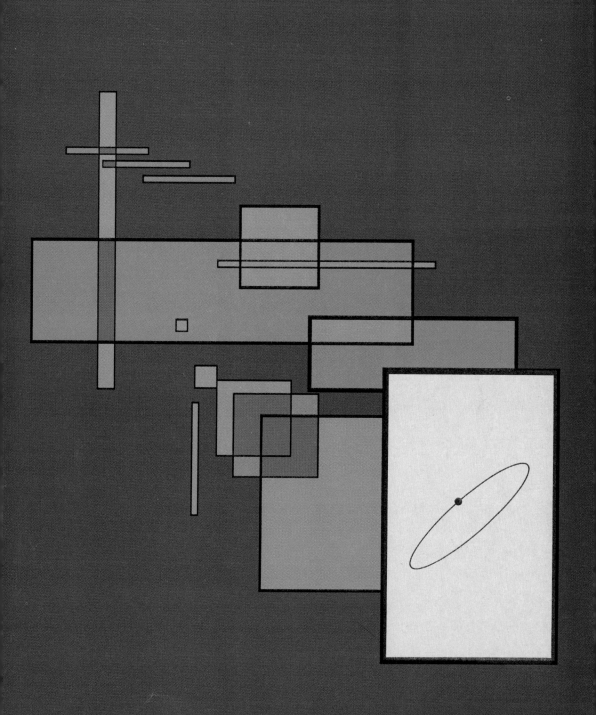

I SURE DON'T CARE FOR SITTIN' OUT HERE IN THE SUN. MY PRICE IS GOING UP BY THE MINUTE. YOU WAIT AND SEE IF IT DOESN'T.

DON'T GET GREEDY. AND HERE THEY COME. GET READY.

POSSUM DARK WATCHED THE HEAT DISTORT THE FLATS. HE DIDN'T CARE FOR THE EFFECT.

HE WAS SUSPICIOUS OF THINGS LESS THAN CUT AND DRIED.

GINNY SWEETHIPS' FLYING CIRCUS

SEX TACOS and DANGEROUS DRUGS

BY NEAL BARRETT, JR.
ADAPTED BY LESLIE CLAGUE AND STEVE NILES
ART : MARK PACELLA
COLORS : SAM PARSONS
LETTERS : M. EISMAN
EDITOR : LETITIA GLOZER

GENTS, YOU'LL BE MORE THAN GLAD YOU WAITED. I'M BRINGING BEAUTY TO THE WASTELANDS, GENTS. LUST THE WAY YOU LIKE IT, PASSION UNRESTRAINED. SEXUAL CRIMES YOU NEVER DREAMED!

GINNY SWEETHIPS, GENTS. GIVING YOU HER INTERPRETATION OF BARBARA JEAN, THE CHEERLEADER NEXT DOOR. INNOCENT AS SNOW, YET A LITTLE BIT WICKED AND WILLING TO LEARN. NOW, WHAT DO YOU SAY TO *THAT*?

NEXT, DEL INTRODUCED NURSE NORA, A SAUCY REDHEAD. AN ANGEL OF MERCY, WEAK AS SOUP IN THE HANDS OF PATIENT PETE.

MOMENTS LATER, HAIR BLACK AS A RAVEN, SHE WAS SCHOOLTEACHER SALLY, COLD AS WELL WATER UNTIL STEVE THE BAD STUDENT LOOSED THE FURY CHAINED WITHIN.

3

WHILE YOU'RE MAKING UP YOUR MINDS, WE HAVE A STARTLING AND ABSOLUTELY FREE DISPLAY OF THE SLICKEST MARKSMANSHIP YOU'LL EVER SEE.

BUDDA-BUDDA-BUDDA

POSSUM STOOD AND BOWED. THE MEN SAW SIX-FOOT-NINE AND A QUARTER INCHES OF HAPPY MARSUPIAL FURY.

DOUBTS WERE SWEPT ASIDE. FUN TODAY WAS CLEARLY NOT FOR FREE.

GENTLEMEN, START YOUR ENGINES. I'LL BE RIGHT HERE TO TAKE YOUR FEE. ENJOY A HOT TACO WHILE YOU WAIT YOUR TURN AT GLORY. HAVE A LOOK AT OUR DISPLAY OF PHARMACEUTICAL WONDERS.

5

DEL SNIFFED EACH GALLON, IN CASE SOME BUFFOON THOUGHT WATER WOULD GET HIM BY.

DEL SOLD TACOS AND DANGEROUS DRUGS, TAKING WHAT HE COULD IN TRADE.

THE DRUGS WERE DIFFERENT COLORS BUT ALL THE SAME: TWELVE PARTS OREGANO, THREE PARTS RABBIT SHIT, ONE PART MARIJUANA STEMS.

HAVE HER DO THE NURSE. YOU WON'T REGRET IT.

THE SCHOOLTEACHER'S BEST. I NEVER SEEN THE LIKE. I DON'T CARE IF SHE'S REAL OR SHE AIN'T.

WHAT'S IN THESE TACOS?

NOBODY YOU KNOW, MISTER.

I COULD USE A HOT BATH AND TOWN FOOD. WHAT YOU FIGURE'S UP THE ROAD?

EAST BAD NEWS.

WELCOM to BEAUTIFULL EAST BAD NEWS

I'M NOT REAL LITTLE AND DON'T GUESS I'M ANY LADY. YOU OPEN FOR BUSINESS OR JUST TALK?

MY NAME'S MORO GAIN. NEVER TURN BUSINESS AWAY IF I CAN HELP IT.

MORO'S REPAIRS
ARMAMENTS • MACHINERY
ELECTRONICS OF ALL KINDS •

WHAT CAN I DO FOR YOU, LITTLE LADY?

YOU DO CONFIDENTIAL WORK?

SECRET'S MY MIDDLE NAME. MIGHT COST A LITTLE MORE, BUT YOU GOT IT. DRIVE IT ON IN AND WE'LL TAKE A LOOK.

DEL, GO FIND US A PLACE TO STAY.

20

NOT THE MOTOR. BACK HERE.

SMELLS A LITTLE RAUNCHY RIGHT NOW. CAN'T HELP THAT 'TIL WE HOSE 'ER DOWN.

SOMETHIN' ELSE!

BACK HERE'S THE PROBLEM.

SENSORY TAPES? WELL, I'LL BE A SON OF A BITCH!

I'VE GOT THREE TAPES, A BRUNETTE, A REDHEAD AND A BLONDE. FOUND A WHOLE CACHE IN ARDMORE, OKLAHOMA. LOOKED AT THREE OR FOUR HUNDRED TO FIND GIRLS THAT LOOKED LIKE ME. SPLICED 'EM DOWN TO SEVEN MINUTES EACH.

LITTLE NEEDLE COMES UP OUT OF THE MATTRESS. STICKS THEM IN THE ASS. SEVEN MINUTE DOSE.

JESUS, THEY EVER CATCH YOU AT THIS, YOU ARE *COOKED*, LADY.

I WASN'T SURE RIGHT OFF IF YOU WERE REAL. NOW, I THINK MAYBE YOU ARE.

IT'S DEL WHO'S THE DROID, NOT ME. WIMP IX SERIES. THE CUSTOMERS THINK IT'S ME, NEVER LOOK AT HIM. SO--THIS SLIPS A LITTLE. MAYBE I GOT A SHORT, HUH?

I'LL HAVE TO GET IN THERE AND SEE. LISTEN, I'D LIKE TO TAKE YOU TO DINNER.

WELL, SURE YOU WOULD.

I'VE GOT MY PRIDE. I DON'T INTEND TO ASK YOU MORE THAN THREE OR FOUR TIMES.

YOU'VE GOT A BIT OF PROMISE. IF I *WANTED* TO HAVE DINNER WITH SOME GUY, YOU'D MAYBE FIT THE BILL.

HELL WITH YOU, LADY. I DON'T NEED THE COMPANY THAT BAD.

⑨

22

I'LL BET THAT MORO GAIN KNEW RIGHT WHERE THIS STORM'D BE.

I DON'T KNOW. SEEMED LIKE A DECENT SORT TO ME.

THAT'S WHAT I MEAN. YOU CAN'T TRUST A MAN LIKE THAT AT ALL.

VEHICLES TO PORT. COMING RIGHT AT US, HAULING TIMBER.

FORT PRU
GAMES OF CHANCE & AMUSEMENT
TERM·WHOLE LIFE·HALF LIFE·DEATH

I DON'T LIKE IT.

YOU DON'T LIKE ANYTHING'S STILL ALIVE. THEY'RE JUST HORNY--I THINK WE'LL DO SOME BUSINESS HERE.

11

YOU GOT A WHORE INSIDE OR NOT? YOU DON'T HAVE TO GIVE US THE PITCH. WE'RE SHOW BUSINESS FOLK OURSELVES. I'M FRED, HEAD ACTUARY.

HEAVY BOND, LINEN WEAVE. NO. 2S, WITH ERASERS, CLAIM FORMS, MAIM FORMS, FORMS OF EVERY SORT.

AND *YOU* GOT GAS IN THAT TRAILER. I CAN SMELL IT FROM HERE. FRIEND, WE CAN SURE TALK BUSINESS WITH YOU THERE. I GOT SEVENTEEN GUZZLERS RUNNIN' DRY.

GASOLINE GREED WAS WHAT IT WAS, AND DEL KNEW THESE MEN WERE BENT ON MORE THAN FLESHLY PLEASURE.

THE GAS IS NOT FOR TRADE. SEX AND TACOS AND DANGEROUS DRUGS IS WHAT WE SELL.

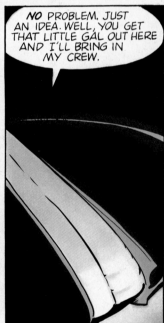

NO PROBLEM. JUST AN IDEA. WELL, YOU GET THAT LITTLE GAL OUT HERE AND I'LL BRING IN MY CREW.

DEL KNEW WITH ANDROIDIAL DREAD THAT WHEN THEY COULD, THE INSURANCE MEN WOULD MAKE THEIR PLAY.

12

IT SEEMED TO BE GOING WELL. CHEERLEADER BARBARA AWOKE FORGOTTEN WET DREAMS, SET THEM UP FOR SALLY THE TEACH AND NORA NURSE.

WE SURE OUGHT TO TALK ABOUT GAS. THAT'S WHAT WE OUGHT TO DO.

TRIED TO. THEY GOT NO USE FOR OFFICE SUPPLIES.

I TOLD YOU, THE GAS ISN'T FOR TRADE, GO TALK TO THOSE REFINERY BOYS, SAME AS US.

THAT'S NOT MY PROBLEM.

MAYBE IT IS.

I KNOW WHAT YOU ARE, MY FRIEND. USED TO HAVE A CPA DROID JUST LIKE YOU, BEFORE THE WAR.

MAYBE WE CAN TALK.

26

⑬

GODDAMN, TRY THE NURSE! NEVER HAD NOTHIN' LIKE IT IN MY LIFE!

HUHDUHDUH.

SHE'S A TIGER. 'SCUSE ME A MINUTE.

SOMETHIN' ISN'T RIGHT HERE, DEL. IT'S GOTTA BE THE TAPES. THAT MORO FELLOW'S A CHEAT.

WE GOT TROUBLE INSIDE AND OUT. THE HEAD WANTS OUR GAS-- WE'D BETTER CLEAR OUT WHILE WE CAN.

THAT'LL RILE 'EM FOR SURE. GIVE ME A MINUTE. I'LL TRY THE THIRD TAPE.

14

JESUS! WHAT'S THAT?!

ROCKETS.

WOOMPH!

BUDDA! BUDDA! BUD

POW! POW!

DON'T TELL ME YOU'RE OUT OF AMMO, POSSUM DARK. THAT STUFF'S PLENTY HARD TO GET. WE'RE FLAT DEAD IS WHAT WE ARE.

16

MORO'S GAIN

RATAPATATARATARATÁ

WELL, IF THAT WASN'T JUST IN THE NICK OF TIME.

I HATE CHOW DOGS. THEY GOT BLACK TONGUES AND THAT'S A FACT.

IN A MOMENT, IT WAS OVER. A FEW UNDERWRITERS MADE IT TO COVER. FORT PRU FLED IN SECTIONAL DISARRAY.

17

I HOPE YOU FOLKS ARE ALL RIGHT. FRIEND, LOOKS AS IF YOU'VE THROWN AN ARM.

NOTHING REAL SERIOUS.

I'M GRATEFUL. GUESS I GOT TO TELL YOU THAT.

WELL, THAT PESKY SHEPHERD'S SORTA RESPONSIBLE FOR THE WHOLE TROUBLE. GOT A LITTLE PISSED WHEN THAT POSSUM CLEANED HIM OUT.

FIVE-CARD STUD, I THINK IT WAS.

I CAN FIX HIM.

YOU'VE ABOUT FIXED ENOUGH, SEEMS TO ME.

I'M REAL EMBARRASSED ABOUT THIS. THAT DOG GOT MAD AND KINDA SCREWED UP YOUR GEAR.

YOU LET A *DOG* REPAIR MY STUFF?

PERFECTLY GOOD TECHNICIAN--IF YOU DON'T GET HIS DANDER UP. SET YOUR TAPES IN A LOOP AND SPED 'EM UP. WORKS OUT TO MACH 7 SEX. COULD CAUSE BODILY HARM.

I'LL SEE ABOUT CHANGING THOSE TIRES. WE OUGHT TO GET DEL OUT OF THE SUN. YOU THINK ABOUT FINDING SOMETHING NICE TO WEAR TO DINNER. EAST BAD NEWS IS KINDA PICKY.

END

31

PROLOGUE:

ON TIMOTHY CLARY'S
NINTH BIRTHDAY HE
GOT NO CAKE.

ALL HE HAD TO EAT
WERE STALE DANISH
PASTRIES FROM THE
BUFFET WAGON...

...AND HE WAS
FEARFULLY
EMBARRASSED
BECAUSE HE
HAD WET HIS
PANTS.

THREE
TIMES.

GETTING TO THE TOILETS
WAS JUST ABOUT IMPOSSIBLE.

DEPARTURES

JOHN F. KENNEDY INT'L AIRPORT

TIMOTHY'S MOTHER HAD GONE
SOMEWHERE TO TRY TO CALL
HIS FATHER. THEN THERE
HAD BEEN A SURGE WHEN
THREE 747's AT ONCE HAD
ANNOUNCED BOARDING,
AND TIMOTHY HAD BEEN
CARRIED FAR FROM
WHERE HE HAD
BEEN LEFT.

GET AWAY! RUN! HIDE!
PRAY AS HARD AS YOU CAN!

WORSE THAN THAT, TIMOTHY WAS VERY SICK.

Frederik Pohl's

FERMI AND FROST

...ATTEMPTED COUP IN CUBA ESCALATED QUICKLY INTO A TACTICAL NUCLEAR EXCHANGE BETWEEN U.S. AND SOVIET SUBMARINES.

SPECIAL REPORT

HAVANA

CNN NEWSWATCH

ADAPTED BY: BRENT ERIC ANDERSON
LETTERS BY: KURT HATHAWAY
EDITED BY: LETITIA GLOZER

HARRY MALIBERT WAS ON HIS WAY TO A BRITISH INTERPLANETARY SOCIETY SEMINAR IN PORTSMOUTH WHEN HIS FLIGHT WAS EMBARGOED BY SOME OFFICIAL SOMEWHERE.

HIS RED AMBASSADOR CLUB CARD HAD ONLY PROTECTED HIS RELATIVE SOLITUDE FOR A FEW HOURS.

WHEN THE FOOD AND DRINK IN THE MAIN TERMINALS BEGAN TO RUN OUT THE AMBASSADOR CLUB WAS OPENED TO EVERYONE

YOU'RE HARRY MALIBERT. I HEARD YOU LECTURE ONCE, AT NORTHWESTERN.

YOU SHOWED SLIDES OF ARECIBO. YOU SAID THAT RADIO TELESCOPE COULD SEND A MESSAGE AS FAR AS ANDROMEDA... IF THERE WAS ANOTHER AS GOOD TO RECEIVE IT.

YOU REMEMBER VERY WELL.

YOU MADE A BIG IMPRESSION.

IT REALLY SOUNDED WONDERFUL, LISTENING FOR MESSAGES FROM SPACE...

...MAYBE MAKING CONTACT...

...YOU MADE ME WONDER WHY WE HAVEN'T HEARD FROM THEM ALREADY.

"MAYBE NOW WE KNOW WHY, "

PLEASE STAND BY

DOCTOR MALIBERT...

CNN SPECIAL BULLETIN

This is a Special Bulletin . . . Please

THIS IS A SPECIAL BULLETIN FROM CNN NEWSWATCH...

...THE PRESIDENT HAS CONFIRMED THAT A NUCLEAR ATTACK HAS BEGUN AGAINST THE UNITED STATES.

"IF THE BOMBS GO OFF THEN *SETI** WILL BE ENDED FOR A GOOD LONG TIME. "

*SEARCH FOR EXTRA-TERRESTRIAL INTELLIGENCE.

③

INCOMING MISSILES HAVE BEEN DETECTED OVER THE ARCTIC.

THIS JUST CAME IN...

WE'VE LOST THE TRANSMISSION FROM SAN FRANCISCO.

IT'S BEGUN.

I CAN GET YOU OUT OF HERE.

AN UNANNOUNCED ICELANDIC DC-10. THERE'S ROOM FOR YOU, DR. MALIBERT.

CAN I PUT THE BOY ON INSTEAD?

TAKE HIM WITH YOU, OF COURSE. I DIDN'T KNOW YOU HAD A SON.

I DON'T, MALIBERT THOUGHT TO HIMSELF, BUT HE HELD THE BOY IN HIS LAP AS TENDERLY AS IF HE WERE HIS OWN.

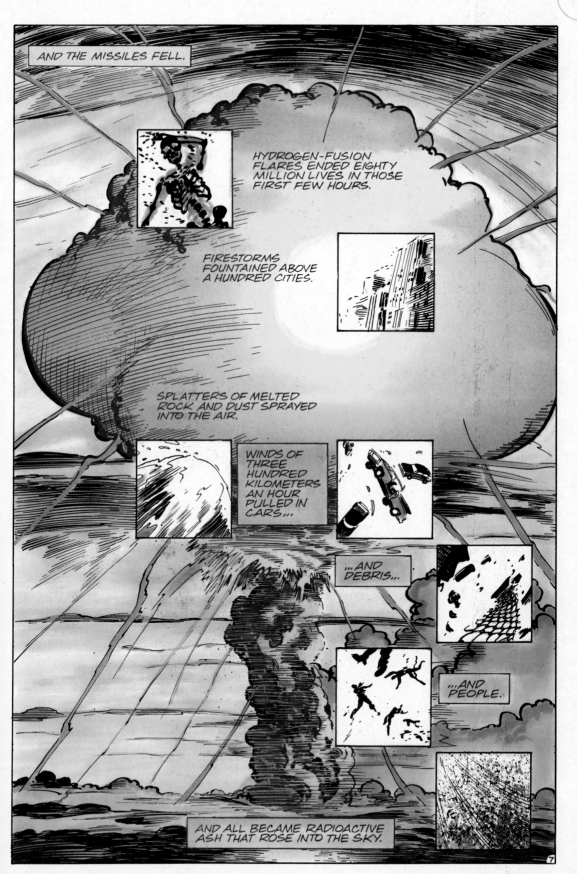

AND THE MISSILES FELL.

HYDROGEN-FUSION FLARES ENDED EIGHTY MILLION LIVES IN THOSE FIRST FEW HOURS.

FIRESTORMS FOUNTAINED ABOVE A HUNDRED CITIES.

SPLATTERS OF MELTED ROCK AND DUST SPRAYED INTO THE AIR.

WINDS OF THREE HUNDRED KILOMETERS AN HOUR PULLED IN CARS...

...AND DEBRIS...

...AND PEOPLE.

AND ALL BECAME RADIOACTIVE ASH THAT ROSE INTO THE SKY.

AND THE SKY DARKENED.

THEN IT GREW DARKER STILL.

KEFLAVIK
INTERNATIONAL AIRPORT

HÄLT

IMMIGRATION

HE'S MY SON. MY WIFE HAS HIS PASSPORT, BUT I DON'T KNOW WHERE MY WIFE IS.

YA, IS GONE, CHICAGO. AND PITTIS-BURRUG, AND CERTAINLY NEW YORK TOO.

IS BAD.

DON'T WORRY, TIMMY. THEY WOULDN'T BOTHER BOMBING REYKJAVIK.

BUT SOMEBODY HAD DECIDED TO TAKE OUT THE U.S. AIRBASE AT KEFLAVIK.

MALIBERT WAS RIGHT. THE RUSSIANS WOULDN'T HAVE BOMBED REYKJAVIK--ON PURPOSE--

--BUT A FORTY-MILE MISS DID THE JOB ANYWAY.

THE HUMAN RACE ALWAYS LIVES EIGHTY DAYS FROM STARVATION.

AND AN ADDITIONAL FORTY DAYS FROM EXTINCTION.

EVERY ANIMAL THAT COULD BE WAS SLAUGHTERED FOR ITS PROTEIN...

...AND ALL HAD TO BE EATEN BEFORE IT SPOILED.

SEEDLINGS POKED UP THROUGH THE DARK EARTH FOR SUNLIGHT, FOUND NONE, DIED.

IT TOOK TROOPS TO CONVOY CORN.

SO THE CITIES STARVED FIRST. AND AS THEY STARVED, THE RIOTS BEGAN.

BEFORE LONG, IT TOOK KILLING.

THE NEXT WAVE OF VICTIMS DIDN'T DIE OF HUNGER.

THEN IT COULD NOT BE DONE AT ALL.

THEY DIED OF SOMEONE ELSE'S.

BY THE END OF "SUMMER" EACH CITY WAS SURVIVED BY A FEW THOUSAND SKINNY, FREEZING DESPERADOES...

STARVED PREDATORS SCRATCHED GRUBS FROM DEAD TIMBER.

...EACH GUARDING THEIR TROVE OF FOODSTUFFS.

MEN COULD WALK ACROSS THE FROZEN THAMES AND THE HUDSON -- THE HWANG HO AND THE MISSOURI.

SOME OF THE PREDATORS WERE HUMAN.

THE WORST WAS THE DARKNESS.

AND THE RAIN.

THE RAIN FELL IN TORRENTS, SHEETS, CASCADES, TURNING TO SNOW AS THE WINTER DARK DEEPENED.

HARRY WAS PUT TO WORK CALCULATING HEAT-LOSS AND PUMPING RATIOS FOR THE PIPED GEOTHERMAL WATER THROUGH THE -30°C CHILL TO THE GREENHOUSES.

SOLAR-SPECTRUM INCANDESCENTS FLOODED THE GROWING TRAYS OF VEGETABLES AND GRAINS WITH PHOTONS...

...WHILE HERDS OF SHEEP WERE COLLECTED AND SLAUGHTERED AND STORED OUTSIDE IN THE WORLD'S DEEP-FREEZE.

IT WAS A BLESSING THAT REYKJAVIK HAD BEEN NUKED--IT MEANT HALF A MILLION FEWER PEOPLE TO FEED.

HARRY HELD MEETINGS IN THE GASTHUIS WHERE HE LIVED WITH TIMOTHY.

THEY PLOTTED STRIKE MAPS--UNTIL THE DEATHS FROM COLD OUTWEIGHED THOSE FROM BLAST. ISOTHERM MAPS--UNTIL THE FREEZING LINE REACHED THE EQUATOR. FATALITY MAPS--UNTIL THEY BECAME TOO FRIGHTENING TO PLOT.

WE DON'T KNOW HOW LONG, HOW COLD, HOW KILLING THE NUCLEAR WINTER WILL BE.

WE DON'T KNOW THE MEGA-TONNAGE OR WHAT ATMOSPHERIC CHANGES HAVE TAKEN PLACE.

WE ONLY KNOW IT WILL BE BAD.

ON THE RARE TIMES THEY TALKED OF SPACE AND **SETI**, TIMMY LISTENED CLOSELY.

AND DREAMED OF RADIO MESSAGES FROM WEIRD ALIENS.

OR WORLDSHIPS THAT COULD CARRY A MILLION PEOPLE ACROSS A HUNDRED THOUSAND YEARS.

TO HEAR A VOICE FROM ANOTHER STAR... THAT WOULD HAVE BEEN FINE.

THERE ARE NO VOICES. NOT EVEN OURS NOW. WE HAVE THE ANSWER TO THE FERMI PARADOX.

WHAT'S THE FERMI PARADOX?

IT IS A THEORY NAMED AFTER ENRICO FERMI, A SCIENTIST.

"FERMI SAID, SINCE THERE ARE BILLIONS OF STARS LIKE OUR SUN, AND OURS HAS PLANETS, OTHER STARS MUST HAVE PLANETS TOO.

"AND SINCE ONE OF OUR PLANETS HAS LIVING THINGS ON IT -- GERMS AND TREES AND HORSES AND PEOPLE -- FERMI WAS CERTAIN OTHER PLANETS HAVE LIFE TOO.

"MAYBE EVEN PEOPLE AS SMART AS US, OR SMARTER, WHO CAN BUILD SPACESHIPS OR SEND MESSAGES, AS WE CAN."

VERY GOOD, TIMMY. I CAN SEE YOU UNDERSTAND.

WELL, FERMI ASKED THE QUESTION, "WHY HAVEN'T SOME OF THESE PEOPLE COME TO SEE US?"

LIKE IN THE MOVIES, THE FLYING SAUCERS.

THOSE MOVIES ARE MADE-UP STORIES, TIMMY. LIKE JACK AND THE BEANSTALK, OR OZ.

CREATURES FROM SPACE MAY HAVE COME TO SEE US, BUT THERE IS NO GOOD EVIDENCE THAT THIS IS SO.

"WE MUST ASSUME THEY HAVEN'T. SO THERE ARE ONLY THREE POSSIBLE ANSWERS TO DOCTOR FERMI'S QUESTION.

"ONE, THERE IS NO OTHER LIFE.

"TWO, THERE IS, BUT THEY WANT TO LEAVE US ALONE.

"AND THE THIRD REASON..."

43

...IS THAT AS SOON AS PEOPLE GET SMART ENOUGH TO GET INTO SPACE, THEY ALSO BUILD TERRIBLE WEAPONS AND KILL THEMSELVES OFF BEFORE THEY GROW UP.

LIKE NOW.

DANGER

THE WORLD WAS ETERNALLY DARK NOW. THE RAINS AND SNOWS HAD LONG SINCE STOPPED, SO NOTHING CAME THROUGH THE CLOUDS BUT FAINT LIGHT FROM THE AURORA BOREALIS.

WHEN THE CALL CAME TO EVACUATE AN INJURED CHILD FROM STOKKSNES, ELDA, A NURSE, BEGGED SPACE FOR HARRY AND TIMMY.

DADDY HARRY! LOOK!

IS THAT ONE OF THE THINGS THAT TALK TO THE STARS?

NO, TIMMY. WE'RE TOO FAR NORTH HERE TO SEE THE WHOLE SKY.

MALIBERT SADLY THOUGHT OF THOSE OTHER PLACES-- ARECIBO, WOOMARA, SOCORRO--BROKEN, RUSTED, WASHED AWAY. ALL THOSE EYES ON SPACE BLINDED NOW.

BUT HE WAS GLAD THAT, FOR THE FIRST TIME, TIMOTHY HAD CALLED HIM "DADDY."

EPILOGUE:

ONE ENDING TO THE STORY IS THAT THE SUN CAME BACK TOO LATE. ICELAND HAD ULTIMATELY STARVED AND FERMI'S TERRIBLE THIRD ANSWER WAS THE RIGHT ONE.

BUT THERE EXISTS ANOTHER ENDING. THE SUN CAME BACK JUST BARELY IN TIME AND TIMOTHY LIVED TO GROW UP.

HE MARRIED ONE OF HARRY AND ELDA'S DAUGHTERS, AND OF THEIR DESCENDANTS-- MAYBE A DOZEN GENERATIONS LATER-- ONE WAS ALIVE ON THAT DAY WHEN FERMI'S PARADOX BECAME A QUAINTLY AMUSING OLD WORRY.

ON THAT DAY THE SKIES SPOKE, AND THOSE WHO LIVED IN THEM CAME TO CALL.

THE NEW HUMAN RACE CHOSE NOT TO EXTINGUISH ITSELF INTO THE DARK.

THEY SURVIVED, AND SAVED ALL THE SCIENCE AND BEAUTY OF LIFE, AND GREETED THEIR STAR-BORN VISITORS WITH JOY...

THE END

GRAPHIC ALBUMS FROM ECLIPSE

1. SABRE by Don McGregor and Paul Gulacy
   (1978) 48 pp, 8 1/2 x 11, b&w
   - 1st edition saddle stitched paperback: 20.00
   - 10th Ann. edition trade paperback: 6.95
   - 10th Ann. ed. signed limited cloth: 25.95
2. NIGHT MUSIC by P. Craig Russell
   (1979) 48 pp, 8 1/2 x 11, b&w
   - saddle stitched paperback: 10.00
3. DETECTIVES, INC. by Don McGregor and Marshall Rogers
   (1980) 48 pp, 8 1/2 x 11, b&w
   - trade paperback: 10.00
4. STEWART THE RAT by Steve Gerber, Gene Colan, and Tom Palmer
   (1980) 48 pp, 8 1/2 x 11, b&w
   - trade paperback: 8.00
5. THE PRICE by Jim Starlin
   (1981) 48 pp, 8 1/2 x 11, b&w
   - saddle stitched paperback: 25.00
6. I AM COYOTE by Steve Englehart and Marshall Rogers
   (1984) 64 pp, 8 1/2 x 11, full colour
   - trade paperback: 25.00
7. THE ROCKETEER by Dave Stevens
   (1985) 72 pp, 8 1/2 x 11 full colour
   (1st printing trade paperback and hardbound out of print)
   - 2nd printing trade paperback: 8.95
   - 2nd printing clothbound: 20.95
8. ZORRO IN OLD CALIFORNIA by Nedaud and Marcello
   (1986) 64 pp, 8 1/2 x 11, full colour
   - trade paperback: 7.95
   - hardbound: 12.95
9. THE SACRED AND THE PROFANE by Ken Steacy and Dean Motter
   (1987) 128 pp, 8 1/2 x 11, full colour
   - trade paperback: 15.95
   - clothbound: 25.95
   - clothbound signed limited edition: 36.00
10. SOMERSET HOLMES by Bruce Jones, April Campbell, and Brent Anderson
    (1987) 128 pp, 8 1/2 x 11, full colour
    - trade paperback: 15.95
    - clothbound: 25.95
    - clothbound signed limited edition: 36.00
11. FLOYD FARLAND, CITIZEN OF THE FUTURE by Chris Ware
    (1987) 48 pp, 7 x 10, b&w
    - trade paperback: 3.95
12. SILVERHEELS by Bruce Jones, Scott Hampton, and April Campbell
    (1987) 64 pp, 8 1/2 x 11, full colour
    - trade paperback: 8.95
    - hardbound: 15.95
    - hardbound signed limited edition: 25.95
13. THE SISTERHOOD OF STEEL by Christy Marx and Peter Ledger
    (1987) 72 pp, 8 1/2 x 11, full colour
    - trade paperback: 9.95
    - clothbound: 15.95
    - clothbound signed limited edition: 25.95
14. SAMURAI, SON OF DEATH by Sharman DiVono & Hiroshi Hirata
    (1987) 48 pp, 8 1/2 x 11, b&w
    - trade paperback: 4.95
15. TWISTED TALES edited by Bruce Jones and April Campbell
    (1987) 48 pp, 7 x 10, full colour
    - trade paperback: $4.95
16. AIR FIGHTERS CLASSICS VOL. 1: The Origin of

Airboy edited by Catherine Yronwode
   (1987) 64 pp, 7x 10, b&w
   - trade paperback: 4.95
17. VALKYRIE, PRISONER OF THE PAST by Charles Dixon, Paul Gulacy, and Will Blyberg
    (1988) 76 pp, 7 x 10, full colour
    - trade paperback: 7.95
    - clothbound signed limited edition: 30.95
18. AIR FIGHTERS CLASSICS VOL. 2: The Origin of Skywolf edited by Catherine Yronwode
    (1988) 64 pp, 7x 10, b&w
    - trade paperback: 4.95
19. SCOUT: THE FOUR MONSTERS by Timothy Truman and Thomas Yeates
    (1988) 136 pp, 7 x 10, full colour
    - trade paperback: 15.95
    - clothbound signed limited edition: 36.00
20. AIR FIGHTERS CLASSICS VOL. 3: Secrets of the Bird Plane edited by Catherine Yronwode
    (1987) 64 pp, 7 x 10, b&w
    - trade paperback: 4.95
21. XYR by Stuart Hopen, Ben Dunn, Frank Giacoia, and Jim Mooney
    (1988) 48 pp, 7 x 10, b&w
    - trade paperback: 4.95
22. ALIEN WORLDS edited by Bruce Jones and April Campbell
    (1988) 48 pp, 7 x 10, full colour
    - trade paperback: 4.95
23. AIR FIGHTERS CLASSICS VOL. 4: Bombs over Boston edited by Catherine Yronwode
    (1988) 64 pp, 7 x 10, b&w
    - trade paperback: 4.95
24. HEARTBREAK COMICS by David Boswell
    (1988) 48 pp, 8 1/2 x 11, b&w
    - trade paperback: 5.95
25. ALEX TOTH'S ZORRO VOL. 1 by Alex Toth
    (1988) 120 pp, 8 1/2 x 11, b&w
    - trade paperback: 10.95
    (for clothbound, see Vol. 2, below)
26. ALEX TOTH'S ZORRO VOL. 2 by Alex Toth
    (1988) 120 pp, 8 1/2 x 11, b&w
    - trade paperback: 10.95
    - clothbound vols. 1 and 2 signed limited edition, together in one slipcase: 55.00
27. SHE by H. Rider Haggard, adapted by Dick Davis and Vincent Napoli
    (1988) 64 pp, 7 x 10, b&w
    - trade paperback: 5.95
28. BROUGHT TO LIGHT by Alan Moore, Bill Sienkiewicz, Joyce Brabner, Thomas Yeates, and Paul Mavrides
    (1988) 80 pp, 8 1/2 x 11, full colour
    - trade paperback: 9.95
    - clothbound: 30.95
29. MIRACLEMAN: BOOK ONE by Alan Moore, Garry Leach, and Alan Davis
    (1988) 80 pp, 7 x 10, full colour
    - trade paperback: 10.95
    - clothbound: 30.95
30. REAL LOVE: The Best of the Simon and Kirby Romance Comics edited by Richard Howell
    (1988) 160 pp, 8 1/2 x 11, b&w
    - trade paperback: 13.95
31. PIGEONS FROM HELL by Robert E. Howard, Adapted by Scott Hampton
    (1988) 64 pp, 8 1/2 x 11, full colour
    - trade paperback: 8.95
    - clothbound signed limited edition: 30.95
32. TEENAGED DOPE SLAVES AND REFORM SCHOOL GIRLS edited by Dean Mullaney

   (1988) 112 pp, 8 1/2 x 11, b&w
   - trade paperback: 10.95
33. BOGIE by Claude Jean-Philippe and Patrick Lesueur
    (1988) 64 pp, 8 1/2 x 11, full colour
    - trade paperback: 10.95
34. AIR FIGHTERS CLASSICS VOL. 5: Blasting Berlin to Bits edited by Catherine Yronwode
    (1988) 64 pp, 7 x 10, b&w
    - trade paperback: 4.95
35. INTO THE SHADOW OF THE SUN: RAEL by Colin Wilson
    (1988) 48 pp, 8 1/2 x 11, full colour
    - trade paperback: 8.95
36. ARIANE AND BLUEBEARD by Maurice Maeterlinck, adapted by P. Craig Russell
    (1988) 48 pp, 7 x 10, full colour
    - trade paperback: 4.95
    - clothbound signed limited edition: 30.95
37. AIR FIGHTERS CLASSICS VOL. 6: The Nazi Youth Kultur edited by Catherine Yronwode
    (1989) 64 pp, 7 x 10, b&w
    - trade paperback: 4.95
38. DR WATCHSTOP: ADVENTURES IN TIME AND SPACE by Ken Macklin
    (1989) 64 pp, 8 1/2/ x 11, full colour
    - trade paperback: 8.95
    - clothbound signed limited edition: 30.95
39. JAMES BOND 007: PERMISSION TO DIE VOL. 1 by Mike Grell
    (1989) 48 pp, 7 x 10, full colour
    - trade paperback: 4.95
40. JAMES BOND 007: PERMISSION TO DIE VOL. 2 by Mike Grell
    (1989) 48 pp, 7 x 10, full colour
    - trade paperback: 4.95
41. JAMES BOND 007: PERMISSION TO DIE VOL. 3 by Mike Grell
    (1989) 48 pp, 7 x 10, full colour
    - trade paperback: 4.95
42. JAMES BOND 007: LICENSE TO KILL by Mike Grell, Chuck Austen, Thomas yeates, & Stan Woch
    (1989) 48 pp, 8 1/2 x 11, full colour
    - trade paperback: 8.95
    - clothbound: 30.95
43. TAPPING THE VEIN VOL. 1 by Clive Barker, adapted by Craig Russell, Chuck Wagner, Fred Burke, and Scott Hampton.
    (1989) 48 pp, 7 x 10, full colour
    (1st printing (gold foil) sold out)
    - trade paperback 2nd printing (green foil): 7.95
44. THE HOBBIT: BOOK 1 by J. R. R. Tolkien, adapted by Charles Dixon and David Wenzel
    (1989) 48 pp, 8 1/2 x 11, full colour
    - trade paperback: 5.95
45. TOADSWART D'AMPLESTONE by Tim Conrad
    (1989) 122 pp, 8 1/2 x 11, b&w
    - trade paperback: 10.95
    - clothbound signed limited edition: 36.00
46. TAPPING THE VEIN VOL. 2 by Clive Barker, adapted by Chuck Wagner, Fred Burke, Klaus Janson, and John Bolton
    (1989) 48 pp, 7 x 10, full colour
    - trade paperback: 7.95
45. LARRY MARDER'S BEANWORLD by Larry Marder
    (1989) 122 pp, 7 x 10, b&w
    - trade paperback: 10.95
    - clothbound signed limited edition: 31.00

SEND TWO FIRST CLASS STAMPS FOR A COMPLETE CATALOGUE OF ECLIPSE GRAPHIC ALBUMS, COMICS, AND TRADING CARDS.

All graphic albums are shipped postpaid. Most are cover price plus postage and handling, but prices on some older albums have been adjusted to reflect scarcity, dwindling stocks, and rising collector values.

Check off items required above and send payment in U.S. funds to:

ECLIPSE BOOKS, P.O. BOX 1099, FORESTVILLE, CALIFORNIA 95436

NAME_____
ADDRESS_____
CITY_____
STATE_____ ZIP_____

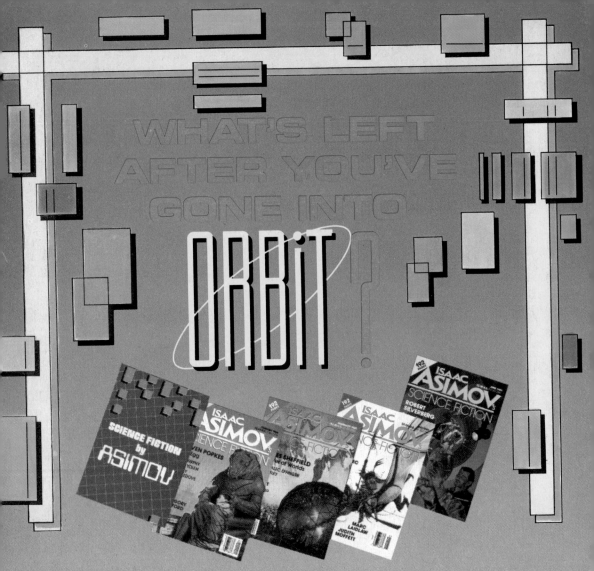

MAKE THE LEAP . . . from the pages of *Orbit*, the world's foremost graphic SF anthology, to the pages of *ISAAC ASIMOV'S SCIENCE FIC-TION MAGAZINE!* *Locus Magazine* hailed IAsfm as *"the magazine on the cutting edge with the newest ideas and writers."* Our award-winning fiction includes stories by Roger Zelazny, Robert Silverberg, John Varley, Connie Willis, Harlan Ellison, Lucius Shepard, William Gibson—and, of course, Isaac Asimov! Each new issue will excite and surprise you, as you join our monthly voyage to worlds beyond imagination. And if you sub-scribe now, you'll receive a bonus gift book: *Science Fiction by Asimov*, featuring some of the Grandmaster's best stories, including one written especially for subscribers of the magazine!

What's left after you leave *Orbit*? The adventure of your life . . .